M000158368

Specific Skill Series

Drawing Conclusions

Richard A. Boning

Fifth Edition

HELEN J. McCORKLE ELEMENTARY SCHOOL
4421 SOUTH STATE STREET
CHICAGO, ILLINOIS 60609

SRA/McGraw-Hill
Columbus, Ohio

Cover, Back Cover, James D. Watt/Masterfile

SRA/McGraw-Hill

A Division of The **McGraw·Hill** *Companies*

Copyright © 1997 by SRA/McGraw-Hill. All rights reserved.
Except as permitted under the United States Copyright Act, no
part of this publication may be reproduced or distributed in any
form or by any means, or stored in a database or retrieval
system, without prior written permission from the publisher.

Printed in the United States of America.

Send all inquiries to:
    SRA/McGraw-Hill
    8787 Orion Place
    Columbus, OH 43240-4027

ISBN 0-02-687983-2

  8 9 IPC 03 02

To the Teacher

PURPOSE:

DRAWING CONCLUSIONS helps develop one of the most important interpretive skills. Pupils learn to look beyond the writer's literal statements to reach an unstated but logical conclusion based on those statements and sometimes their phrasing. In DRAWING CONCLUSIONS the correct conclusion is the most logical one for pupils to reach from only the information presented.

FOR WHOM:

The skill of DRAWING CONCLUSIONS is developed through a series of books spanning ten levels (Picture, Preparatory, A, B, C, D, E, F, G, H). The Picture Level is for pupils who have not acquired a basic sight vocabulary. The Preparatory Level is for pupils who have a basic sight vocabulary but are not yet ready for the first-grade-level book. Books A through H are appropriate for pupils who can read on levels one through eight, respectively. **The use of the *Specific Skill Series Placement Test* is recommended to determine the appropriate level.**

THE NEW EDITION:

The fifth edition of the *Specific Skill Series* maintains the quality and focus that has distinguished this program for more than 25 years. A key element central to the program's success has been the unique nature of the reading selections. Nonfiction pieces about current topics have been designed to stimulate the interest of students, motivating them to use the comprehension strategies they have learned to further their reading. To keep this important aspect of the program intact, a percentage of the reading selections have been replaced in order to ensure the continued relevance of the subject material.

In addition, a significant percentage of the artwork in the program has been replaced to give the books a contemporary look. The cover photographs are designed to appeal to readers of all ages.

SESSIONS:

Short practice sessions are the most effective. It is desirable to have a practice session every day or every other day, using a few units each session.

SCORING:

Pupils should record their answers on the reproducible worksheets. The worksheets make scoring easier and provide uniform records of the pupils' work. Using worksheets also avoids consuming the exercise books.

It is important for pupils to know how well they are doing. For this reason, units should be scored as soon as they have been completed. Then a discussion can be held in which pupils justify their choices. (The Integrated Language Activities, many of which are open-ended, do not lend themselves to an objective score; thus there are no answer keys for these pages.)

GENERAL INFORMATION ON *DRAWING CONCLUSIONS*:

The questions in DRAWING CONCLUSIONS do not deal with direct references; thus the answers do not use the same words as the paragraphs. On the Picture Level, the readers examine the picture for the correct answer. The Preparatory, A, and B levels contain primarily indirect references; that is, the answers are found in the paragraphs but with slightly different wording. Some easy conclusions are also included. As the books advance in challenge, there are more difficult conclusions, involving less obvious relationships. The conclusions also become more dependent on qualifying words such as "mostly," "all," "some," or "only."

In DRAWING CONCLUSIONS the readers are asked to find an <u>example</u>, note a <u>contrast</u>, <u>generalize</u>, see <u>cause</u> and <u>effect</u> relationships, detect a <u>mood</u>, see an <u>analogy</u>, identify a <u>time</u> or <u>place</u> relationship, make a <u>comparison</u>, or <u>anticipate</u> an <u>outcome</u>.

It is important that the teacher ask pupils to find in the paragraph the specific information relevant to the tentative conclusion. Then pupils must test the conclusion against the information provided. When the emphasis is placed on finding evidence to prove answers and when the pupils put themselves in roles of detectives, not only does their ability to draw conclusions rapidly improve, but they also have fun.

Pupils must know that a conclusion is a judgment made. It must be supported by strong evidence. In DRAWING CONCLUSIONS the correct answer is one that is either highly likely or certain.

Some alternate answer choices may be true. The answer that is accepted as correct, however, must not only be true but must have supportive evidence in the paragraph. The clue may hinge on a single word, involve a phrase or a sentence, or encompass the paragraph as a whole.

RELATED MATERIALS:

Specific Skill Series Placement Tests, which enable the teacher to place pupils at their appropriate levels in each skill, are available for the Elementary (Pre-1–6) and Midway (4–8) grade levels.

About This Book

A writer does not tell you everything in a story. Sometimes you need to figure out things that are not told. You do this by thinking about what the writer does tell you. This is called **drawing a conclusion**. A conclusion is what you can tell from what the writer tells you.

Good readers draw conclusions as they read. They think about what the writer tells them. Read this story. Think about what you can tell from what the writer says. Try to draw a conclusion about the differences between donkeys and horses.

> Donkeys look like small horses with huge ears. Like horses, donkeys have been helping people for thousands of years. They pull carts and carry heavy loads.

Did you figure out that a donkey's ears are bigger than those of a horse? Did you also figure out that most horses are bigger than donkeys? You can draw these conclusions from the clues the writer gives.

In this book, you will read short stories. After you read each story, choose the answer that is something you can tell from the information in the story. Remember to use clues in the story to draw a conclusion.

1.   It is possible to make music without playing an instrument. One way is to blow across the top of a bottle. You can make different sounds by using different size bottles. You may be surprised at the sounds you make!

2.   Elephants have a long life span. Some live to be sixty years old. Elephants lose teeth as they age. Then they must find vegetation that is tender to eat. An old elephant that loses all its teeth cannot chew and will die.

3.   Have you ever heard anyone say, "Many hands make light work"? This is an old saying. It means that if many people help to do a job, no one person has to work very hard. The work becomes easy or light.

4.   The hippo is a large water and land animal. It lives in Africa. Except for the elephant, the hippo is the heaviest of all land animals. A large hippo may weigh as much as three automobiles. We wouldn't want a hippo to step on our toes!

5.   Some people say that salt water never freezes. This isn't true. Salt water does freeze. However, it takes a colder temperature to freeze salt water than it does to freeze fresh water. Salt water freezes at twenty-eight degrees. Fresh water freezes at thirty-two degrees.

1. You can make sounds—

    (A) that no one has ever heard
    (B) with different bottles
    (C) by rubbing blades of grass

---

2. An elephant without teeth—

    (A) dies of disease
    (B) dies of starvation
    (C) dies from a hunter's bullets

---

3. The opposite of the saying would be—

    (A) "Few hands make no work."
    (B) "Few hands are made to work."
    (C) "Few hands make heavy work."

---

4. You can tell that the hippo weighs—

    (A) less than an elephant
    (B) more than an elephant
    (C) the same as an elephant

---

5. The freezing temperatures of salt and fresh water differ by—

    (A) ten degrees
    (B) four degrees
    (C) twenty degrees

1. Young birds don't seem to know what to eat. They will peck at anything. Put a stick near them and they will open their mouths and beg. Their mothers and fathers show them what to eat by picking up food and dropping it in front of them.

---

2. How would you like to see everything upside down? It might be fun for just a little while. There are glasses that make everything look upside down. The glasses were made so that people can learn more about the eyes and just how the brain helps the eyes see.

---

3. Baby robins never stop eating. They are always hungry. They keep the mother and father robin busy bringing them worms. During a single day, a young robin eats more than its own weight in food. It eats fifteen feet of worms!

---

4. Snow helped the American Indians to hunt by slowing down fast animals. It also made it easier for Indians to see and follow animal tracks. At the same time, however, animals were better able to see the Indians who trailed them. Indians couldn't get very close without being seen.

---

5. You probably don't think of weeds as good food. Yet, in Japan, many people use seaweed as a part of their regular diet. Often they dry it and roll it around rice. This dish is called sushi. Sometimes Japanese people eat plain seaweed as a snack.

UNIT 2

1. A baby bird is likely to—

    (A) peck at a pencil

    (B) never peck at anything

    (C) eat nothing

2. People who wear upside-down glasses are likely to—

    (A) get mixed up

    (B) see no change

    (C) have better balance

3. To feed a young robin each day takes—

    (A) less than fifteen feet of worms

    (B) fifteen feet of worms

    (C) more than fifteen feet of worms

4. The snow helped—

    (A) only the American Indians

    (B) only the animals

    (C) both the American Indians and the animals

5. People in Japan—

    (A) plant seaweed for fun

    (B) think seaweed is good for people

    (C) eat many kinds of weeds

1.   People can live without food for more than a month. They can live without water for about a week. Of course, people living in the desert must have water much sooner than that. People can live without air for only about six or eight minutes.

---

2.   Did you ever try to sleep standing up? How about while hanging upside down? If you were a cow or a bat, you would not find such ideas strange at all. Cows often sleep standing in a field. Bats sleep hanging upside down in caves or trees.

---

3.   Many people think that deserts are made up just of sand. This is not true. In most deserts sand covers only a small part of the land. Sometimes sand covers only one or two miles of every ten. Most of the deserts are covered by rock.

---

4.   It takes a chicken about nine weeks to weigh three pounds. In those nine weeks the chicken must eat about seven pounds of food. Many years ago chickens had to eat about twelve pounds of food for about fourteen weeks before they weighed three pounds.

---

5.   Some people cannot see very well at night. They are said to be night-blind. They have to be careful if they go out when it's dark. They can see better at night if they eat a lot of eggs, sweet potatoes, butter, and carrots.

1. People need food—

   (A) sooner than they need water

   (B) every day

   (C) not as soon as they need air

2. You can tell that—

   (A) bats hang by their teeth

   (B) animals sleep in different ways

   (C) cows often fall down in their sleep

3. Of every ten miles of desert, rock covers—

   (A) about one mile

   (B) about five miles

   (C) eight or nine miles

4. Chickens of today—

   (A) eat less and gain more weight

   (B) have fewer feathers

   (C) don't gain weight

5. People's sight at night—

   (A) is never good

   (B) can improve

   (C) cannot be improved

1.   Many birds must eat stones with their food. They can't chew the hard grain they eat because they have no teeth. Instead of chewing, they swallow tiny stones. As the stones and food mix together in their stomach, the stones grind up the food.

2.   It takes a turtle about ten hours to travel one mile. A snake can travel two miles in one hour. A house cat can travel about thirty miles in an hour. A jack rabbit can travel forty-five miles in an hour.

3.   A magnet is a piece of metal that pulls other metals toward it. Did you ever try to fish with a magnet? You won't catch any fish. You may get something better. Tie a line to the magnet and drop it to the bottom. You may pull up something worth far more than a fish!

4.   A bee can move its wings very fast. In just one second it can move its wings about two hundred times. So can a housefly. A wasp can move its wings even faster. It moves them about three hundred times in a second!

5.   In the mountains of one country the farmers own very big horns. The horns are twice as big as the farmers. The alpenhorns, as they are called, are often twelve feet long. The farmers use them to make loud signals that can be heard far away.

1. You can tell that—

    (A) all birds eat stones

    (B) some birds have teeth

    (C) the stones do not hurt the birds

2. Cats move more slowly than—

    (A) turtles

    (B) snakes

    (C) jack rabbits

3. You may pick up something made of—

    (A) wood

    (B) stone

    (C) iron

4. Bees and houseflies move their wings—

    (A) faster than anything that flies

    (B) faster than wasps

    (C) at the same speed

5. It is likely that small horns would—

    (A) make just as loud a sound

    (B) make even louder sounds

    (C) not make as loud a sound

1. Did you ever see "snow in summer"? There is a plant with this name. It is a low plant that covers the ground like a blanket of snow. The flowers are white. The leaves are gray. Take a look. You really will see "snow in summer."

_____

2. There are many rats in the world. No one knows just how many rats there are. Many rats live under the ground. Many live in other places where they can't be seen. Some people say there are about as many rats in the world as there are people.

_____

3. People and birds don't walk in the same way. The bird's heel or back part of its foot is lifted high into the air. Birds walk only on their toes. Most often birds have four toes. People walk with their heels on the ground.

_____

4. Certain plants trap and eat insects. Some of these plants have a sweet juice inside them. Insects enter to drink the juice and get stuck inside. Other insect-eating plants have sharp leaves. When an insect lands on a leaf, the leaf snaps shut.

_____

5. It is fun to turn over a big rock on the beach. Make sure you turn the rock back to the position it was in before you moved it. If you don't turn it back over, all the sea animals under it or clinging to the underside will die.

1. The "snow in summer"—

   (A) doesn't look like real snow

   (B) doesn't feel like real snow

   (C) is as cold as real snow

2. You can tell that no one has—

   (A) seen a rat

   (B) counted all the rats

   (C) counted all the people

3. You can tell that most birds have—

   (A) more toes than people have

   (B) bigger toes than people have

   (C) fewer toes than people have

4. Some insects get trapped because they—

   (A) like sweet juice

   (B) can't fly

   (C) eat sharp leaves

5. You can tell that rocks—

   (A) hurt sea animals

   (B) won't be found on beaches

   (C) protect sea animals

1. Look at the colors of road signs. Blue signs tell of nearby hospitals, telephones, or camping grounds. Red signs say "stop" or "don't travel into these roads or lanes." Green signs tell of crossroads or bike trails. Yellow signs warn of changes ahead. Orange signs tell about road repairs.

---

2. Some birds fly against a closed window. They don't see the glass. If you see a bird who has hit a window, don't touch it. It may die of fright. Let the bird rest. It is likely that the stunned bird will fly away in just a few minutes.

---

3. Did you know that the horn of a rhinoceros is made of hair? The hair is so tightly twisted together that it seems solid. A rhinoceros can knock over cars and break into houses with its horn. Some rhinoceros horns are over four feet long!

---

4. In very big cities of long ago it wasn't easy to get a glass of fresh milk. There was only one way to be certain of getting it. That was to get it right from the cow. Cows were driven through the streets and milked in front of the buyer's door.

---

5. The butterfly flower comes in many colors—white, pink, brown, blue, and yellow. So do butterflies. The flowers are shaped like a butterfly's wings. They are between one inch and two inches wide. These plants must be handled as carefully as you would handle a butterfly.

1. You can tell that road signs have—

   (A) special colors

   (B) good pictures

   (C) bright lights

---

2. Most birds who hit windows—

   (A) die right away

   (B) live

   (C) later die of a broken neck

---

3. You can tell that a rhinoceros horn is—

   (A) curved

   (B) strong

   (C) shiny

---

4. People of long ago didn't know how to—

   (A) keep milk fresh

   (B) milk cows

   (C) buy milk

---

5. From the story you can't tell—

   (A) where the plant grows

   (B) the color of the plant

   (C) the shape of the flowers

A. Exercising Your Skill

Do you like riddles? You may not know it, but when you solve a riddle, you are **drawing a conclusion**. A conclusion is a guess you make. The guess is based on facts. Read these riddles. Think about the facts each riddle gives. Then write the answers on your paper.

1. Which weighs more, a pound of feathers or a pound of bricks?
2. What doesn't get any wetter no matter how hard it rains?
3. What time of day is spelled the same backward or forward?
4. What goes around a yard but doesn't move?
5. How can you tell the difference between a can of tomato soup and a can of chicken soup?
6. What is the difference between *here* and *there*?
7. How many apples can you put into an empty bag?
8. What is dark but is made by light?
9. How much dirt is there in a hole exactly one foot deep and one foot across?
10. What has four fingers and a thumb but is not a hand?

B. Expanding Your Skill

Take turns reading and answering the riddles. Did everyone come up with the same answers? Why or why not? Talk with your classmates about the facts you used to solve the riddles. Then turn this page upside down to check the answers to the riddles.

Answers: 1. neither—they weigh the same; 2. ocean, lake, river, pond; 3. noon; 4. a fence; 5. read the label; 6. the letter t; 7. only one—then the bag is no longer empty; 8. a shadow; 9. none; 10. a glove

C. Exploring Language

What makes a joke funny? In order to understand a joke, you need to draw a conclusion about the facts in it. Read these jokes. On your paper, answer the questions about the jokes.

1. Al's teacher asked him which state was his favorite. "California," he said. "How do you spell *California*?" she asked him. Al thought a bit and said, "I really like Ohio much better!"

    Why did Al change his mind about which state was his favorite?

2. Sue's mother told her, "It's time for dinner. Go wash your hands." "Do I have to wash both of them?" Sue asked. "No, just one—if you can!" her mother answered.

    What did Sue's mother mean?

3. Silly Willy told a friend that his doctor had said to drink carrot juice after a hot bath. His friend asked how the carrot juice tasted. "I don't know yet," said Silly Willy. "I'm still drinking the hot bath."

    What had Silly Willy's doctor really wanted him to do with the hot bath?

D. Expressing Yourself

Choose one of these things.

1. Make up your own riddles to ask your classmates. See if they can guess the answers to your riddles by using the facts you give. Ask them how they thought of their answers.

2. Put on a joke show with some of your classmates. Take turns telling jokes to the rest of the class. If you don't know any jokes, find a book of jokes in the library.

1. Sharks have teeth with edges like the edges of saws. The sharks often lose their teeth but get new ones so fast there is not time for the teeth to lose their cutting edges. When teeth get torn out, an extra row of teeth behind them just moves forward.

2. Not all birds' eggs hatch. Not all of the baby birds live. Some people think that about one of every five eggs hatches. If all the eggs hatched and all the birds lived, the whole earth would be covered with birds and their nests.

3. Some big things are light. Some small things are heavy. A big balloon is lighter than a small toy. A big bag of popcorn may be lighter than a small bag of candy. A small pail of sand may be heavier than a large pillow.

4. The housefly carries many germs. Some of the germs are on the hairs of its legs. Some are on the housefly's feet. Most flies carry far more than a million germs. One fly was known to carry over six million germs!

5. When you buy something today, you pay with money. Long ago, people didn't use money. Instead, they traded with valuable goods. For example, Indians in South America once used cocoa beans as money. They believed the beans had special powers.

UNIT 7

1. You can tell that—

   (A) sharks' teeth have handles like saws
   (B) sharks' teeth are always very sharp
   (C) many humans have teeth like sharks

2. You can tell that—

   (A) most eggs don't hatch
   (B) most eggs do hatch
   (C) half the eggs hatch

3. From the size of things we—

   (A) can't always tell the color
   (B) can't always tell the weight
   (C) can tell the age

4. You can tell that a germ is—

   (A) bigger than a fly
   (B) smaller than a fly's feet
   (C) bigger than a fly's feet

5. Long ago, Indians—

   (A) bought things with cocoa beans
   (B) liked the smell of cocoa beans
   (C) made food from cocoa beans

1.　There is a plant that helps people tell the time. This plant is about three feet high. Its flowers may be white, red, yellow, or pink. These flowers open in the late afternoon. The flowers close in the morning. The plant is named the "four-o'clock."

_____

2.　Did you ever have so much to carry that you wished you had an extra hand? The spider monkey uses its tail almost like an extra hand. For example, it can swing from trees by its tail. That leaves its hands free to pick up and throw objects.

_____

3.　Raindrops may seem very big. Yet they are so small that it would take one hundred of the smallest to make an inch. It takes four of the biggest raindrops to make an inch. Raindrops don't get bigger than a quarter of an inch. They just break into smaller drops.

_____

4.　Horses don't live as long as people. A horse that lives to the age of thirty is very old. One year of a horse's life is equal to three years of a person's. A thirty-year-old horse is as old as a person who is ninety.

_____

5.　Make a picture of your room in your mind. Keep the middle of the picture clear. Make the sides of the picture blurred. Scientists say that this is the way babies see things. The middle of what babies look at is clear. Things away from the middle are not clear.

1. This plant clock—

   (A) is poorly named

   (B) has a minute hand

   (C) is well named

2. The spider monkey—

   (A) holds on to branches with its tail

   (B) uses its tail to climb

   (C) throws coconuts for fun

3. The biggest raindrops are—

   (A) about a quarter of an inch

   (B) bigger than an inch

   (C) much smaller than a quarter of an inch

4. A horse of ten is equal in age to a—

   (A) ten-year-old child

   (B) thirty-year-old person

   (C) three-year-old baby

5. Grownups see things—

   (A) just the way a baby does

   (B) opposite to the way a baby does

   (C) in a different way from a baby

1. Pumpkins had been growing for thousands of years before they were used to make pumpkin pies. The American Indians taught the early settlers how to cook pumpkins. The settlers later added eggs, milk, and sweetening to the cooked pumpkin and baked it in a pie shell.

2. Many kinds of fish from the deep sea cannot see. They are blind. Good eyesight would not help them. The deep sea is darker than night. It is too dark to see in. Fish that are blind smell and feel their way through the water.

3. Can you imagine wearing a shirt made out of tree bark? Long ago, some people who lived in forests made cloth from bark. They soaked the bark in water and then beat it with rocks to make it soft. Sometimes they dyed it with berry juice. Then they shaped it into clothes.

4. Pine cones were once the favorite toys of many Indian children. The cones were easy to find. They had many uses. Pine cones were good to play catch with. They were also used in contests to see who could throw them the highest, the farthest, and the straightest.

5. The body of an octopus is soft. The only hard part of the octopus is its beak. The beak is like that of a parrot. Because it is soft, an octopus can get away from its enemies by squeezing itself through very narrow cracks and under rocks.

UNIT 9

1. The early settlers invented the—

   (A) cooked pumpkin

   (B) jack-o'-lantern

   (C) pumpkin pie

2. You can tell that some fish need—

   (A) no light in order to see

   (B) some light in order to see

   (C) good eyesight in the deep sea

3. Some people who made clothes from bark—

   (A) did not need warm clothing

   (B) wanted nice-looking shirts

   (C) sewed with wooden needles

4. Pine cones took the place of—

   (A) all toys

   (B) balls

   (C) a fire engine

5. The octopus is lucky that—

   (A) it has no enemies

   (B) its body is soft

   (C) it has a beak

1.   Cows have baby cows about once a year. A baby cow is called a calf. After a calf has been born, the cow will give milk for about ten months. If the cow doesn't give birth to a calf, the cow won't give any milk.

2.   People need to take in about two and a half quarts of liquid every day. They get about a quart from the food they eat. Fruits and vegetables are mostly water. They get the other quart and a half from drinking liquids of all kinds.

3.   Long ago the best road in America was the Boston Post Road. It ran between Boston and New York City. It took George Washington more than a week to make a trip between the two cities. Today, with an automobile, it takes about five hours.

4.   When sunfish are born, it takes more than ten of them to make an inch. When fully grown, a sunfish may be over six feet long. The sunfish gets to be over seven hundred times as big as it was when it was born.

5.   Basketball was first thought up by a teacher. He needed a game for his students to play indoors in the winter. The teacher made up a set of rules, nailed a basket to the wall, and split the students into teams. Soon the students were passing the ball and shooting for baskets.

UNIT 10

1. You can tell that most cows—

    (A) give milk all year long

    (B) don't give milk two months a year

    (C) have baby cows three times a year

2. People get most of their water—

    (A) by drinking liquids

    (B) from fruits

    (C) from vegetables

3. It was a slow trip long ago because—

    (A) Washington didn't want to get there

    (B) the cities were farther apart

    (C) there were no automobiles

4. From the story you can tell that sunfish—

    (A) are big when they are born

    (B) grow to be seven hundred feet

    (C) grow a lot

5. You can tell that the students—

    (A) quickly learned the new game

    (B) lived where it was warm all year

    (C) had played basketball before

1. When a baby is born, its heart beats about 140 times a minute. In children about ten years old, the heart beats about ninety times a minute. Later on, the heart beats about eighty times a minute. In grownups the heart beats about seventy times per minute.

---

2. Have you ever entered your pet in a pet show? Often the smallest and largest pets win prizes. Usually the funniest, prettiest, and most well-behaved pets win prizes too. If the show includes a talent contest, the pet that does the cleverest trick wins a prize.

---

3. Your skin only looks smooth. Take a look at it through a special glass that makes things look bigger. You will see a countless number of valleys and long chains of mountains. These valleys and mountains are tiny lines.

---

4. One fish looks as if it has big eyes near its tail. These eyes look much bigger than the real eyes, which are on its head. Enemies take a bite at the big eyes. Instead of biting the head, they just nip the tail. The fish often swims safely away.

---

5. It helps to put sawdust into a birdhouse. Some birds don't gather their own nesting material. An inch of sawdust or a little more is enough. The sawdust makes a good bottom for the nest. The sawdust also stops eggs from rolling out.

1. Children's hearts beat—

   (A) **faster than grownups'**

   (B) **280 times a minute**

   (C) **slower than grownups'**

---

2. You can tell that—

   (A) **pet shows are usually for dogs and cats**

   (B) **most pet shows have more than one winner**

   (C) **most pets are owned by children**

---

3. You can tell that—

   (A) **skin is smooth**

   (B) **skin is sometimes rough**

   (C) **things are not always as they appear**

---

4. The "eyes" near the tail—

   (A) **are real**

   (B) **look real**

   (C) **are small**

---

5. The sawdust serves—

   (A) **no purpose**

   (B) **a hundred purposes**

   (C) **two purposes**

1.   As we grow, our skin has to grow also. As we get bigger, our skin gets bigger. The skin of an insect cannot do this. It cannot grow or stretch. It is a hard shell. An insect has to get rid of its shell before it can grow.

---

2.   How would you like to wear a hat that would pop open and form an umbrella? There once was such a hat. It came in handy in bad weather. Another hat was made that helped people see in the dark. This hat lighted up.

---

3.   Did you know that airmail letters were sent long, long ago? Did you know that they were sent by the people of Egypt, thousands of years before the very first airplane was made? The people of Egypt used birds to carry their mail.

---

4.   People have changed the color of their hair for centuries. They have done this with colors made from vegetables. Today people find it easier to change the color of their hair. They can simply wash their hair with a special shampoo and their hair color will change.

---

5.   More than a hundred years ago, some orange bugs with black dots were sent to America from Australia. The bugs began eating insects that harmed orange-growing trees. In two years, the bugs, called ladybirds, had eaten enough of the harming insects to save the orange trees of America!

1. The skin of an insect doesn't grow because it—

   (A) isn't soft
   (B) is just like our skin
   (C) is a different color

2. You can tell that some hats had—

   (A) no purpose
   (B) an extra purpose
   (C) no one to wear them

3. Airmail letters of today are likely to—

   (A) travel more slowly
   (B) be sent to closer places
   (C) arrive sooner

4. You can tell that—

   (A) all people like the color of their hair
   (B) no people like the color of their hair
   (C) people sometimes like to change their looks

5. You can tell that—

   (A) Australia had no harming insects
   (B) the harming insects were killing the orange trees
   (C) the harming insects were bigger than ladybirds

A. Exercising Your Skill

The word *bee* is on each of the lists below. For each list, draw a **conclusion** about how a bee is like the other things on the list. On your paper, write a group of words, or heading, for each list that tells how the things are alike. Under each list, write the name of one thing that can be added to the list.

1. _____

    bee
    airplane
    bird
    bat

    _____

2. _____

    bee
    flea
    tick
    fly

    _____

3. _____

    bee
    flowers
    butterfly
    bush

    _____

4. _____

    beehive
    spiderweb
    bird's nest
    anthill

    _____

B. Expanding Your Skill

With your classmates, talk about your headings and the words you added to the lists. Did you draw the same conclusions about each list? Talk about how the things in each list are alike. Then make up another list of words that tell about things that are the same in some way. See if your classmates can guess how the things are alike. Have your classmates explain their ideas. Then ask them to name other things that could go on the same list.

C. Exploring Language

The paragraphs below give some facts about bees. For each paragraph, write a conclusion you can draw from the information that is given. Write the conclusion on your paper.

1. There are more than 3,000 different kinds of bees in North America. The honey bee lives in large groups in a hive. So do about fifty other kinds of bees. All the remaining kinds of bees, though, live alone. Some live in old snail shells, and some live in holes in the ground.
   Conclusion: _____

2. Older bees take pollen from flowers and carry it back to the hive to make honey. Younger bees work inside the hive. Some of them take care of the queen bee and the young bees. Others keep the hive clean or guard the entrance to the hive. In hot weather, many of the worker bees have another job—beating their wings to cool the hive.
   Conclusion: _____

3. When a bee finds a place where there is a lot of good food, it flies back to its hive. Then the bee does a dance. The way this bee dances tells the other bees where the food is and how far away it is.
   Conclusion: _____

D. Expressing Yourself

Choose one of these things.

1. Write a few sentences about an insect or other animal that you know something about. Give facts about the animal. Then see if a classmate can draw a conclusion about the animal.

2. Make a page for a class book called "Insect and Animal Homes." Draw a picture and write a few sentences about the animal or insect you choose.

1. Did you ever hear a strange sound coming from the wall? Did it sound like a clock? If so, it may have been made by a beetle. Long ago, people thought the ticking meant that someone was about to die. Thus the beetle is called "the deathwatch beetle."

2. A white buffalo wasn't seen very often on the plains even in the days when there were millions of buffalo. Thus it was that American Indians had strange ideas about the white buffalo. They believed that it could turn itself into a fox, a hawk, or a woman.

3. Have you ever heard someone say, "You are barking up the wrong tree"? Do you know what this saying means? It means that you are looking for something in the wrong place. It means you have to look for it somewhere else.

4. A person can swim about five miles an hour. The little goldfish can swim almost as fast. The whale can swim four times as fast as people. So can the sea turtle. The dolphin swims five times as fast as a person. The sailfish can swim even faster.

5. On a hot day, some people like to float down a river in an old tire. You can do this on America's Delaware River. Most people float for about three miles, at the speed of one mile an hour. Friends tie their tires together and picnic as they travel along.

UNIT 13

1. The sound of this beetle—

   (A) pleased people

   (B) surprised people

   (C) frightened people

2. American Indians believed that white buffalo—

   (A) had magical powers

   (B) were like other buffalo

   (C) could turn a fox into a woman

3. Barking up the wrong tree—

   (A) never happened to anyone

   (B) is a smart thing to do

   (C) is something people do sometimes

4. The sea turtle can't swim—

   (A) at all

   (B) as fast as a sailfish

   (C) as fast as a person

5. Tire rides on the Delaware usually last about—

   (A) three hours

   (B) one hour

   (C) two hours

1. For a very long time people used only the large or capital letters. The use of small letters came about after many years. There was a reason that people began to make small letters. They wanted to save space in books.

_____

2. Many people give blood to blood banks. The blood banks keep the blood for other people who are sick or hurt. Some people like to give blood on their birthdays. They say that doing this makes them more thankful for the good health they enjoy.

_____

3. It isn't easy to paint with most paints. Often the paint drips onto our hands, clothes, or floor. There is a paint that won't drip or run. It is a dripless paint. It sticks to the wall like a mud pie. You just take your brush and spread it out.

_____

4. Good drivers do not go as fast at night as they do during the day. They slow down when cars come toward them. They don't look at the headlights of the other cars. Good drivers stay alert and keep their eyes on the road.

_____

5. When spring comes to Louisiana, many folks begin looking for crawfish. Crawfish are shell-covered creatures found in streams and lakes. To catch crawfish, people get up early in the morning. They use nets or fishing lines.

1. You can tell that some people wanted books with—

    (A) more pages
    (B) fewer pages
    (C) no pages

2. People who give blood—

    (A) must be in good health
    (B) use blood from blood banks
    (C) do it only on their birthdays

3. The dripless paint is—

    (A) hard as a rock
    (B) like soft butter
    (C) just like the old paint

4. You can tell that night driving is—

    (A) easier than day driving
    (B) safer than day driving
    (C) harder than day driving

5. You can tell that crawfish—

    (A) are found under the sand
    (B) are not found in the winter
    (C) are found in the ocean

1.   One beetle gives off lights of two colors. From both ends of its three-inch body it gives off a red light. From other parts it gives off a green light. This beetle is called the railway beetle. Its red and green lights look like railway signals.

2.   Can you tell what part of the United States a person is from just by listening to that person speak? Word detectives say that if you talk for a while they can tell the exact place where you grew up. They claim that certain sayings and words you use give the answer.

3.   A jellyfish isn't made of jelly. It is made mostly of salt water. It must stay in salt water to live. If you cut a piece out of the middle of a jellyfish, the jellyfish can't feel it. It grows back together. The jellyfish is a strange fish.

4.   Did you ever hear of a flyway? A flyway is a path through the air that birds take when they travel each year to and from their winter homes. Millions and millions of birds use some of the flyways each year.

5.   Eggs are a well-liked food all year round, but they have a special meaning in the spring. Long ago, some people believed that the earth was hatched from an egg. They gave each other eggs that had been colored red. The eggs stood for the return of the sun after winter.

UNIT 15

1. This beetle must look somewhat like—

   (A) the moon

   (B) a traffic light

   (C) a turtle

---

2. It is likely that the word detectives know a great deal about—

   (A) people

   (B) speech

   (C) history

---

3. You can tell that jellyfish—

   (A) aren't easy to hurt

   (B) are good to eat

   (C) are all very big

---

4. Flyways are used—

   (A) by very few birds

   (B) by flies

   (C) at certain times

---

5. Some people once believed that—

   (A) the sun was an egg

   (B) red eggs brought good luck

   (C) the earth grew out of an egg

1. Seven-five-three is a special day in November to honor the children of Japan. Children dress up in their finest silk robes. They and their families carry branches of trees to show how grateful they are. They give thanks for having safely reached the ages of three, five, and seven.

---

2. Hawks, owls, foxes, snakes, and skunks like to eat mice. People try to get rid of mice. They try to trap them. Sometimes they offer mice food—poisoned food. Yet there always seem to be more mice to take the place of the dead ones.

---

3. Moscow is a city with a clean-car rule. Drivers can be fined by the traffic police if their cars are not clean enough. It pays to wash your car, or to get someone else to wash it, if you live in Moscow!

---

4. Can you picture a cat that is three times the size of the cats we see most of the time? There is one in England. The cat weighs twenty pounds and is almost three feet long. The owner says that the cat eats only fish and steak.

---

5. If you get a tooth knocked out, and it's not a baby tooth, hurry to your dentist. The dentist may be able to put it back in. Go to the dentist right away. Don't wait more than one hour. You also must keep the tooth wet or moist. It's best to keep it in a damp cloth.

1. Children of Japan feel the excitement of—

   (A) **being born**
   (B) **being alive**
   (C) **singing songs**

2. You can tell that mice should—

   (A) **be on the lookout**
   (B) **live very long lives**
   (C) **eat everything given to them**

3. You can tell that—

   (A) **cars in Moscow are not very old**
   (B) **the police in Moscow check cars for dirt**
   (C) **drivers pay fines for speeding**

4. This cat is about the size of a—

   (A) **horse**
   (B) **dog**
   (C) **bear**

5. It is important to—

   (A) **take your time**
   (B) **save time**
   (C) **keep your tooth dry**

1.   Long ago, people did not write from left to right, as we do today. At first they wrote from right to left. Then they wrote one line right to left and the next line left to right. Later, most people began to write all the lines left to right.

---

2.   Babies can cry from the time they are born. It takes them about five weeks to learn to smile. In seven weeks or so the baby can make some cooing sounds. It takes about twenty-five weeks for a baby to learn to sit up by itself.

---

3.   The coast of Australia is famous for its large clams. It is not uncommon to find clams that weigh one hundred or two hundred pounds. However, the champion of them all weighed in at the surprising total of 580 pounds!

---

4.   The housefly can fly about five miles an hour. The robin can fly six times as fast as the housefly. The little hummingbird can fly about sixty miles an hour. The duck hawk can fly one hundred and seventy miles in an hour.

---

5.   "Whip-poor-WILL!" You hear this song often, but you hardly ever see the bird who sings it and who is named for it. The whippoorwill is brown and tan with a big head, long wings, a rounded tail, and tiny feet. Its bark-colored feathers make it hard to spot in trees.

1. You can tell that in time—

    (A) writing lost its importance

    (B) things stay the same

    (C) things change

2. Babies make cooing sounds—

    (A) before they learn to smile

    (B) after they learn to sit up

    (C) after they learn to smile

3. It must be hard to—

    (A) find the Australian clams

    (B) tell if a clam is Australian

    (C) lift the Australian clams

4. A robin is faster than—

    (A) a hummingbird

    (B) a housefly

    (C) a duck hawk

5. The whippoorwill is hard to find because—

    (A) it flies too high in the sky

    (B) it sits very still in one spot

    (C) it is the same color as tree branches

1. Some animals seem to forget much faster than others. Flies seem to forget very quickly. They can't even remember the place where their enemies live. Flies that have almost been killed by some other insect have returned to the same spot where this happened.

---

2. A razor clam can dig into sand very fast. Clam diggers have to work very quickly or the razor clam will dig down so deep it can't be reached. A razor clam can bury itself in the sand in six or seven seconds.

---

3. While most of us sleep, many people are at work. Under electric lights, millions of people go about their work in hospitals, offices, trucks, TV studios, firehouses, buses, airplanes, and hotels. When the sun comes up, their work is done. For everyone else the day has just begun.

---

4. Bears like sweets even more than people do. There is nothing that tastes better to bears than honey. Bears can easily climb trees. Their thick fur keeps them from being hurt by bee stings. Along with the honey, the bear eats the bees too!

---

5. When your leather boots or shoes get wet, you can dry them with an electric drier. Such driers give a gentle heat that will not cause your shoes to crack or get hard. Hunters often take electric driers on hunting trips.

1. Flies that forget—

    (A) **are sure to be killed**

    (B) **might be killed**

    (C) **will never be killed**

___

2. Slow clam diggers are—

    (A) **good at catching razor clams**

    (B) **much faster than the fastest razor clams**

    (C) **not good at catching razor clams**

___

3. You can tell that the night people—

    (A) **sleep on the job**

    (B) **sleep and play during the day**

    (C) **get tired when the sun goes down**

___

4. You can tell that most people and bears—

    (A) **like one another**

    (B) **look like one another**

    (C) **like some of the same things**

___

5. You can tell that—

    (A) **all driers run on batteries**

    (B) **a high heat can harm leather shoes**

    (C) **most hunters wear rubber boots**

1.   Everyone knows what a penny is. It is just one cent. Did you ever hear of a two-cent coin? Long ago there was a two-cent coin. It was used in our country. About one hundred years ago they stopped making the two-cent coin.

2.   Parts of Chile receive a large amount of rain. In one part it rains an average of 325 days a year. However, in 1916 the people there were amazed at the rain that fell. During that year it rained 348 days, an all-time record.

3.   Many Americans show that they are proud of their country by hanging an American flag outside their homes from Flag Day, June 14, through Independence Day, July 4. These people honor their country in a twenty-one-day salute—flags flying every day during that time.

4.   Are you hungry? How about a nice, tasty leaf? It seems strange to think of people eating leaves. Yet they have been eating leaves for a long time. Lettuce was a favorite food for people two thousand years ago. Lettuce is also well liked today.

5.   Bats eat insects. They eat many of them. In just sixty seconds a bat may go after eight insects. Most of the time the bat gets the insects it goes after. Two of every eight insects the bat chases may get away if they are lucky.

UNIT 19

1. You can tell that coins—

   (A) **may change**
   (B) **never change**
   (C) **are all the same**

2. In parts of Chile it rains—

   (A) **every day**
   (B) **almost every day**
   (C) **every other day**

3. The twenty-one-day salute—

   (A) **happens once a year**
   (B) **takes place twice a year**
   (C) **happens in the fall**

4. You can tell that people's taste—

   (A) **always changes**
   (B) **doesn't always change**
   (C) **is bad**

5. You can tell that insects have—

   (A) **an even chance to get away**
   (B) **less than an even chance to get away**
   (C) **no chance to get away**

A. Exercising Your Skill

A good detective uses clues to draw a conclusion about a crime. A good reader uses clues to draw a **conclusion** about a piece of writing. Try your skill at being a detective. Read each set of clues below. Then, on your paper, write what you think happened.

EVENT 1

sunny day   children playing outdoors

broken window   glass on floor under window

angry person   baseball on rug

What do you think happened? _____

EVENT 2

empty goldfish bowl   water on table

wet paw prints on floor   cat licking its paw

What do you think happened? _____

EVENT 3

chair next to high shelf   crumbs on plate

empty cookie box   crumbs on shirt

sick-looking child   puppy licking child's face

What do you think happened? _____

B. Expanding Your Skill

Compare the conclusions you drew about each event with your classmates' conclusions. Did everyone reach the same conclusions? Talk about the clues you used in each case.

C. Exploring Language

Choose items from the list below. Put some of them together to make a set of clues about an event. Here is one way to do it: green balloon, big pin, loud pop, crying child. You may want to add other items of your own. On your paper, write a few sentences that tell the conclusion you drew about the event. Then read your list to your classmates. (Do *not* read your conclusion.) See if they can tell what happened.

green balloon	dog licking lips	upset chair
hissing cat on table	smiling boy	empty platter
sticky knife and fork	big pin	crumpled rug
hungry man	barking dog	loud pop
broken lamp on floor	chair near table	crying child

D. Expressing Yourself

Choose one of these things.

1. Make up a list of clues about an event. Then trade lists with a classmate. Write a few sentences that draw a conclusion about the event.

2. Write a short story but don't write the ending. Trade stories with a classmate. Write a good ending for the story you now have. Then ask your classmate to tell what he or she thought of your ending and to give reasons for the answer.

3. Work together with a group of classmates. Act out a scene. (This can be a scene from the clues in Part C.) See whether your other classmates can draw a conclusion about what is happening.

1.   The potato is a favorite food around the world. It can be cooked in a different way every day of the year. It can be served for breakfast, lunch, and dinner. Potatoes should be cooked with their skins on. The part of the potato that keeps people well and strong is just under the skin.

2.   Children like to light candles on a birthday cake. Today this is usually done at an afternoon or evening party. Long ago, birthday candles were lighted when the child woke up in the morning. The special candles were kept burning until the cake was eaten later in the day.

3.   A parachute looks like a big umbrella. It is used to slow down the fall of anyone who jumps from an airplane. Even with a parachute, people fall about fifteen feet every second. When they hit the ground, they often are hurt.

4.   Fish have no body heat. If water freezes solid, so do the fish. Some fish can remain alive after being frozen in a block of ice for months. Once the ice melts, the fish swim away as if nothing had happened.

5.   A lake with a very long name is found in Massachusetts. It's called Chargoggagoggmanchauggagoggchaubunagungamaug! Can you say it? It means "You fish on your side. I fish on my side. Nobody fishes in the middle." American Indians of long ago gave the lake its name.

1. You can tell that the potato is—

   (A) a tasteless food

   (B) a breakfast dish

   (C) an amazing vegetable

2. The time when birthday candles are lighted—

   (A) has stayed the same

   (B) has changed

   (C) will never change again

3. Without a parachute a person would fall—

   (A) fifteen feet a second

   (B) sixteen feet a second

   (C) much faster

4. You can tell that—

   (A) all fish can survive in ice

   (B) fish have no blood

   (C) fish are as warm or cold as their surroundings

5. You can tell that—

   (A) American Indians had rules about fishing

   (B) the lake was very large

   (C) the lake did not have many fish

1.   It's best to wait until the end of the day before you buy shoes. If you buy shoes in the morning, they may not be the right size. By the end of the day, standing and walking make your feet somewhat larger.

2.   If you come across a bird with a broken wing or some other injury, put the bird into a paper bag. This will keep it from moving about. Its feathers won't get hurt. Then you can take the bird to someone who can care for it.

3.   Cats catch colds just as people do. Cats that have a cold sneeze very often. Their noses run. Their eyes become watery, like the eyes of people who have colds. When this happens to your cat, keep it warm. Feed the cat lots of liquids.

4.   You can't see air. It has no color. You can't smell air. It has no smell. You can't taste air. It has no taste. You can't see air, but you can see through it. You can feel air when it is moving.

5.   The very first plants lived in the water. To grow on land too, plants had to change. Plant stems became harder and stronger. This let plants stand up straight. The skin of plants also became tougher. This kept the sun and wind from drying the plants out.

1. Shoes bought during the morning may be—

    (A) too soft

    (B) too small

    (C) the wrong color

2. It's best to keep an injured bird—

    (A) in your hands

    (B) in your house

    (C) still

3. You can tell that cats with colds—

    (A) show just one sign

    (B) are somewhat like people

    (C) need no help

4. You can tell that—

    (A) air isn't real

    (B) air is somewhat like a ghost

    (C) people cannot feel air

5. You can tell that plants grow—

    (A) only in the water

    (B) only on land

    (C) in water and on land

1. Some people say that a very hot summer means that a cold winter will follow. People have believed this for many years. If a summer has been hotter than usual, the winter may just seem colder. The idea that a cold winter follows a hot summer isn't true.

2. Antarctica is an island. Most of Antarctica's animals are fish. Birds and sea animals also visit its shores. The largest land animal on the island is an insect similar to the housefly. This insect grows to be only one-tenth of an inch long!

3. Do you like to eat small bits of food off and on during the day? If so, you like to *nosh*. That's a word some people use to mean "nibble on food." People like to nosh on fruit, cheese, bread, rolls, cake, and just about anything.

4. The first bicycle was called a walk-along. It looked a lot like the bicycle of today, but there was something missing. There were no pedals. The riders had to push it along with their feet, like a kiddie car.

5. Hair grows more quickly in the summer than in the winter. It grows faster during the day than at night. People between the ages of seventeen and twenty-four have more hair than they did when they were children or when they become very old.

1. From this story we can say that—

   (A) all beliefs are true

   (B) no beliefs are true

   (C) some beliefs are true

---

2. The land animals in Antarctica—

   (A) grow to be large

   (B) live in the ocean

   (C) are not very big

---

3. You can tell that—

   (A) people can nosh on almost any food

   (B) most people don't like to nosh

   (C) people who nosh stay thin

---

4. You can tell that walk-alongs were—

   (A) faster than the bicycles of today

   (B) prettier than the bicycles of today

   (C) slower than the bicycles of today

---

5. Hair grows best when it is—

   (A) cold

   (B) dark

   (C) warm

1.   The first people to make correct maps were the Egyptians. Before a map can be drawn, land must be measured. The Egyptians made tools for this purpose. They measured the entire land with special measuring chains.

2.   Did you know that "people years" and "dog years" are not the same? Scientists have made up a way to show how much faster a dog's life goes by than a person's. For each "people year," or real year, they count seven "dog years." When a dog is only ten real years old, it is entering old age at seventy "dog years."

3.   Not every letter that is sent goes to the right person. Sometimes the writing is so poor that it can't be read. Sometimes the address isn't right. Each year millions of letters never get to the places the writers wanted them to go to because of mistakes and poor writing.

4.   It is said that people should take a lesson from the clock. The clock passes the time by keeping its hands busy. People who do what the clock does also pass the time by keeping their hands busy and not by sleeping the time away.

5.   A horseshoe crab is often called a king crab, but it isn't a crab at all. The front part of the horseshoe crab is shaped like a horseshoe. A long tail helps it move along the shore. Maybe you have seen the marks it leaves on the beach.

1. You can tell that the very first mapmakers—

    (A) used a lot of skill

    (B) guessed a lot

    (C) knew a lot about chains

2. You can tell that—

    (A) usually people live longer than dogs

    (B) dogs and people live the same number of real years

    (C) dogs live seven times longer than people

3. You can tell that—

    (A) everyone writes clearly

    (B) penmanship isn't important

    (C) people make careless mistakes

4. You can tell that busy people—

    (A) sleep the time away

    (B) don't do what clocks do

    (C) act like clocks

5. The horseshoe crab probably gets its name from its—

    (A) mother

    (B) shape

    (C) color

1.   Do you have any idea of how much air you take in and out of your body each day? It's enough to blow up about six hundred seventy-five beach balls! You could fill ten thousand quart bottles or eleven thousand liters with all that air.

2.   Little babies sleep most of the time. They wake up only for food or to be changed. A one-year-old baby is awake about eight hours of every twenty-four. That means a baby sleeps two of every three hours.

3.   Dogs can hear much better than people. A sound that people can hardly hear at ten feet, dogs can hear at one hundred feet. Dogs can also hear higher sounds than people can. That is why people use very high-pitched whistles to signal to dogs.

4.   You probably know that fish can do things like swim and eat. You might be surprised to know that some fish can also make electricity. The electric eel's body makes enough electricity to run a small motor or to light a lamp!

5.   A good cow gives a lot of milk. It's no wonder! After all, a good dairy cow eats a lot of food. In one year's time a cow eats ten thousand pounds of food. A cow also drinks a lot of water—ten tons a year!

1. Passing in and out of the body every day are—

   (A) **large pieces of dust**

   (B) **enormous amounts of air**

   (C) **small bodies of light**

---

2. One reason babies wake up is that they are—

   (A) **hungry**

   (B) **tired**

   (C) **happy**

---

3. In one way dogs' hearing is—

   (A) **two times better than people's hearing**

   (B) **ten times better than people's hearing**

   (C) **not as good as people's hearing**

---

4. You can tell that—

   (A) **not all fish make electricity**

   (B) **electric eels use lights to see**

   (C) **eels can't swim or eat**

---

5. A cow must spend a lot of time—

   (A) **playing**

   (B) **eating**

   (C) **in the barn**

1.   The earliest people carried things in their arms and on their backs. They also carried light things on their heads when they went from place to place. About eight thousand years ago, people began to tame animals to carry heavy things.

---

2.   Long ago, people didn't take a bath every morning or night. They took a bath just once a week. Bath night was Saturday night. Water was heated on the kitchen stove. It was poured into a washtub, which sat on the kitchen floor.

---

3.   Have you ever heard someone say, "Don't count your chickens before they are hatched"? This really means that it isn't wise to be sure of something before it happens. It is better to wait and see, without being too sure of what will take place.

---

4.   Computers come in many varieties. Some have enough equipment to fill a large room. Others are much smaller. You could carry them in a small suitcase, or even in your hand.

---

5.   Everyone can make music. We don't need music lessons to whistle, sing, or hum with our mouths. We can clap our hands, snap our fingers, or slap our legs. Some people are so good at making this kind of music that they sound like a whole band!

1.   You can tell that animals—

   (A) have always carried things

   (B) have never carried things

   (C) have learned to carry things

2.   People of long ago were—

   (A) never clean

   (B) always clean

   (C) clean at times

3.   From each and every egg—

   (A) we always get a chicken

   (B) we never get a chicken

   (C) we may or may not get a chicken

4.   Computers come in—

   (A) different suitcases

   (B) different rooms

   (C) different sizes

5.   To make music, people—

   (A) can use their own bodies

   (B) need to take lessons

   (C) join a band

A. Exercising Your Skill

An "**is to**" sentence is a way of comparing things. An "is to" sentence shows how things that don't seem to be alike *are* alike in some way. It shows how two sets of things are alike. Read this "is to" sentence:

Kitten is to **cat** as **puppy** is to **dog**.

A kitten is a *baby* cat, and a puppy is a *baby* dog. This sentence shows that this is the way these two sets of things are alike.

Read each sentence below. Draw a conclusion about each set of things. Ask yourself if the sentence makes sense. On your paper, number 1 to 10 and write *sense* or *no sense* to tell whether you think each sentence makes sense.

1. **Happy** is to **glad** as **unhappy** is to **sad**.
2. **Rabbit** is to **hop** as **fish** is to **fly**.
3. **Up** is to **down** as **in** is to **out**.
4. **Green** is to **grass** as **blue** is to **sky**.
5. **Train** is to **track** as **boat** is to **road**.
6. **Bed** is to **bedroom** as **stove** is to **backyard**.
7. **Turtle** is to **slow** as **horse** is to **fast**.
8. **Paint** is to **picture** as **cook** is to **food**.
9. **Doctor** is to **hospital** as **teacher** is to **farm**.
10. **Push** is to **pull** as **warm** is to **hot**.

B. Expanding Your Skill

Talk about the sentences with your classmates. For each sentence that made sense, explain how the two sets of things are alike. For each sentence that did not make sense, tell why it did not. Then write those sentences again. Change them so that they make sense.

C. Exploring Language

In the first three "is to" sentences below, you can choose a word to finish each sentence. First, look at the words in the complete set and figure out how the words go together. Then read the three word choices. Which word goes with the meaning of the sentence? On your paper, write 1 to 3 and the word that completes each sentence.

1. **Hat** is to **head** as **shoe** is to _____ .
   foot   **hand**   **tail**

2. **Soap** is to **wash** as **food** is to _____ .
   drink   **walk**   **eat**

3. _____ is to **fruit** as **dog** is to **animal**.
   Bread   **Water**   **Apple**

You can complete the next three sentences in your own way. Write 4 to 6 on your paper. Figure out what word would fit in the sentence and write it. Afterwards, compare your words with your classmates' words.

4. **Roof** is to **house** as _____ is to **head**.

5. **Row** is to **boat** as **drive** is to _____ .

6. **Long** is to _____ as **light** is to **dark**.

D. Expressing Yourself

Choose one of these things.

1. Make up three "is to" sentences. Write them, but leave out one word in each sentence. Trade papers with a classmate and finish each other's sentences.

2. Make up an "is to" sentence for each of these groups: (1) What Color Something Is, (2) What Shape Something Is, and (3) How Something Is Used. For example, number 1 could be: **Tomato** is to **red** as **banana** is to **yellow**.

HELEN J. McCORKLE ELEMENTARY SCHOOL
4421 SOUTH STATE STREET
CHICAGO, ILLINOIS 60609